Amanda Cant

WORKBOOK

CONTENTS

	VOCABULARY	GRAMMAR	FEATURES
 **UNIT 1** PAGES 4-10	sit down, stand up, talk, clean up, shout, run *the alphabet*	Don't shout. Sit down, please. How do you spell …?	**Country:** Canada **Spelling:** ake **Values Project:** Make a *Polite* Sign
UNIT 2 PAGES 11-19	second, minute, hour, morning, afternoon, evening get up, have breakfast, go to school, have lunch, have dinner, go to sleep	What time is it? It's … o'clock. I … at … o'clock.	**Country:** Germany **Spelling:** ime, ine **Values Project:** Make a Planner
UNIT 3 PAGES 20-26	sheep, chicken, donkey, duck, goat, cow ladybug, grasshopper, caterpillar, mosquito, butterfly, ant	This is / That's a… These / Those are … What's this / that? It's a / an … What are these / those? They're …	**Country:** Kenya **Spelling:** one, ose **Values Project:** Take Care of a Clay Animal
UNIT 4 PAGES 27-35	peppers, carrots, potatoes, onions, beans, tomatoes cookies, French fries, hamburgers, sandwiches, ice pops, pancakes	Do you like …? Yes, I do. / No, I don't. I like … I don't like …	**Country:** Turkey **Spelling:** une, oon **Values Project:** Make a *New Things* Poster
UNIT 5 PAGES 36-42	play the guitar, speak Vietnamese, climb a tree, touch your toes, do taekwondo, jump rope fly, swim, hop, sing, walk, ride a horse	Can you …? Yes, I can. / No, I can't. I / He / She / They can … I / He / She / They can't …	**Country:** South Korea **Spelling:** ea, ee **Values Project:** Make an *I Can* Collage

	VOCABULARY	GRAMMAR	FEATURES

PAGES 43-51

play soccer, watch TV, sing karaoke, play computer games, read books, play board games

draw, make models, listen to music, dance, paint, do puzzles

What do you like doing?
I like …-ing.
I don't like …-ing.

He / She likes …-ing.
He / She doesn't like … -ing.

Country: Argentina
Spelling: ai, ay
Values Project: Make a Friendship Bracelet

PAGES 52-58

house, castle, boat, trailer, apartment, cave

ocean, desert, jungle, woods, city, country

He / She / It lives in …
Where do you live?
I live in …

Country: Mongolia
Spelling: igh, y, ie
Values Project: Make a *Welcome* Sign

PAGES 59-67

piano, trumpet, tambourine, violin, drums, recorder

Sunday, Monday, Tuesday, Wednesday, Thursday, Friday, Saturday

Do you play …?
Yes, I do. / No, I don't.

Does he / she … on …?
Yes, he / she does.
No, he / she doesn't.

Country: Australia
Spelling: oa, ow
Values Project: Make a Promise Card

PAGES 68-74

airplane, bus, helicopter, car, train, motorcycle

Multiples of 10: 10-100

I don't go to … by …
I go by …
He / She doesn't go to … by …
He / She goes by …

How many … are there?
There are …

Country: Thailand
Spelling: ue, ew
Values Project: Make a Display

PAGES 75-83

shirt, pants, skirt, shoes, sweater, sneakers

long, short, big, small, old, new

This is …'s …
These are … 's …
He / She has …

Country: Peru
Spelling: th
Values Project: Make a Sharing Token

PAGES D1–D10   MY DICTIONARY   PAGE 95   PROGRESS RECORD

Lesson 1

VOCABULARY

1 Connect the words and pictures.

1 shout
2 clean up
3 sit down
4 stand up
5 run
6 talk

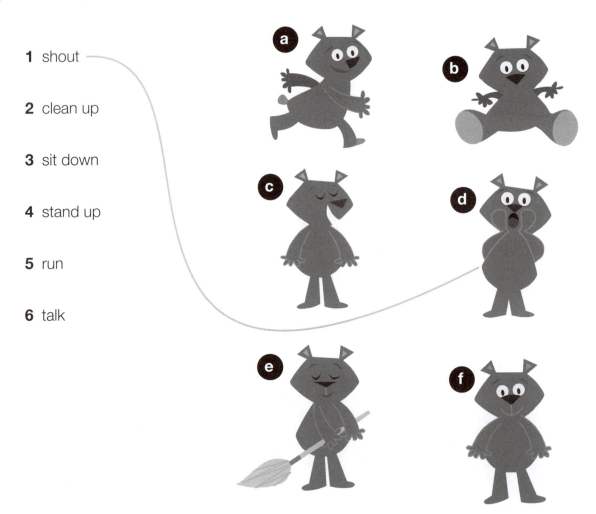

2 Circle the one that's different. Then check (✓).

DICTIONARY page D1

Lesson 2 · GRAMMAR

1 Match the sentences and pictures.

 a
 b
 c
 d
 e 1
 f

1 Stand up, please.

2 Don't shout.

3 Don't sit down.

4 Run, please.

5 Don't talk.

6 Clean up, please.

2 Unscramble and write.

1 nleCa pu, sleeap   C_l_ _e_ _a_ n _u_ _p_, p__ __ __ __ __!

2 tDno klta   D__n'__ __ __l__!

3 notD nur   D__n'__ __ __n!

4 tSi wnod, epeals   S__t __ __w__, __ __ __ __ __e!

Lesson 3

SPELLING

1 Read. Then underline *ake*.

Jake has a cake.

Now Jake's cake is in the lake!

2 Write *ake*. Then connect.

1 There's a sn<u> a </u><u> k </u><u> e </u>.

2 J___ ___ ___ has a c___ ___ ___.

3 Now J___ ___ ___'s c___ ___ ___ is in the l___ ___ ___!

6

Lesson 4

MAKE A POLITE SIGN
Be polite!

VALUES PROJECT

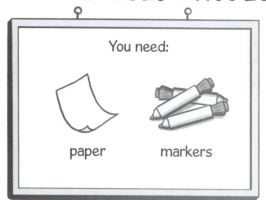

You need: paper, markers

Draw a sign.

Draw a picture and complete the sign.

Write the rule.

Make a display in your classroom or school.

About Me
Are you polite at school and at home?

7

Lesson 5 · VOCABULARY·

1 Circle the letters that sound similar.

1	B	(D)/ O	4	G	Q / E
2	K	C / J	5	I	H / Y
3	V	B / W	6	P	Z / R

2 Spell your name and your favorite animal.

TRACK 7

3 Listen. Then write the letters in the correct color.

G, J = red   E, I = blue   K, W, Y = green

```
A  B  C  D  ___  F  ___

H  ___  ___  ___  L  M  N

O  P  Q  R  S  T  U  V

___  X  ___  Z
```

DICTIONARY
page D1

8

Lesson 6 · GRAMMAR ·

1 Connect the words and pictures. Then spell.

1 chair
2 pencil
3 ruler
4 clock
5 eraser
6 desk

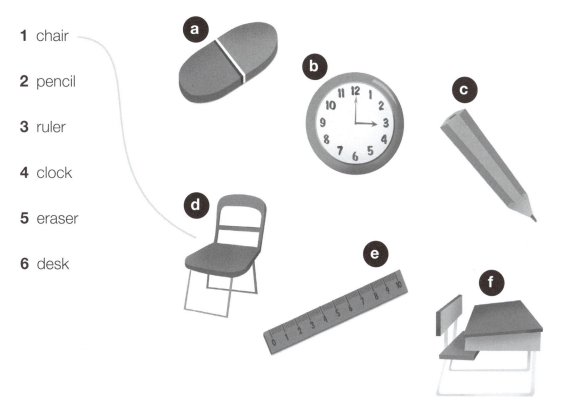

2 Complete the questions. Then write the answers.

1 How ___do___ you spell ?   _e_ r _a_ _s_ er

2 How do you _____  ?   ___ ___l___r

3 _____ do you spell  ?   t___ ___k

4 How do _____ spell  ?   ___h___u___

9

Lessons 7 and 8

LET'S VISIT CANADA

1 Match the questions and answers.

1 What's her favorite sport?   c   a Her name's Sara.

2 What's the national animal of Canada? ○   b Yes, it is.

3 What's her name? ○   c Her favorite sport is ice hockey.

4 Is a beaver brown? ○   d It's the beaver.

2 Now check your answers on page 16 of your Student's Book.

3 Draw a picture of you playing your national sport. Then write.

Hi, I'm _____.

Look. I'm playing _____.

It's the national sport of _____.

Let's play, OK? It's fun!

10

Lesson 1

· VOCABULARY ·

1 Match the words and pictures.

1 morning
2 afternoon
3 evening

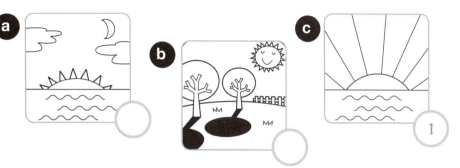

2 Write. Then connect.

1 m___ ___ut___   2 h___ ___r   3 s___ c___ ___d

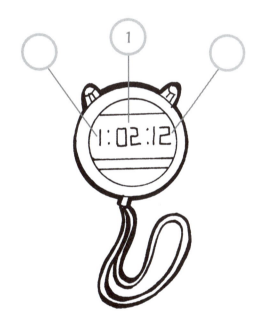

3 Read, solve, and circle.

1 ten seconds + three seconds = thirteen seconds / fifteen seconds
2 seven seconds – six seconds = thirteen seconds / one second
3 five hours + fourteen hours = eighteen hours / nineteen hours
4 eight minutes – two minutes = six minutes / ten minutes
5 twelve minutes + three minutes = nine minutes / fifteen minutes

DICTIONARY
page D2

11

Lesson 2 · GRAMMAR

1 Read and draw.

1 It's seven o'clock.

2 It's eleven o'clock.

3 It's five o'clock.

4 It's three o'clock.

2 Read. Then draw for you.

1 You're at school. What time is it?

2 You're at the park. What time is it?

3 You're in bed. What time is it?

Lesson 3

 SPELLING

1 Read. Then underline *ime* and *ine*.

2 Write *ime* and *ine*.

1 It's n___ ___ ___ o'clock.

2 Do you have a d___ ___ ___?

3 There's a l___ ___ ___!

13

Lesson 4

MAKE A PLANNER

Don't be late!

VALUES PROJECT

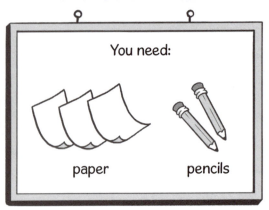

You need: paper, pencils

Fold three pieces of paper to make a book.

Make a planner. Write your name.

Write the days of the week.

Complete your planner with times and activities.

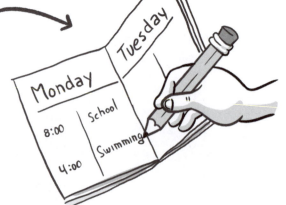

About Me
Are you sometimes late? Why?

Lesson 5 · VOCABULARY·

1 Write. Then match the phrases and pictures.

1 _h_ave _b_reak_f_ast
2 hav___ ___unch
3 g___ to sl___ ___p
4 ha___e di___ne___
5 ___ ___ to s___ ___ool
6 ___et ___p

 1

2 Write the numbers in the correct column.

1 sleep
2 dinner
3 up
4 breakfast
5 school
6 lunch

have …	go to …	get …
	1	

TRACK 19

3 Listen and circle.

1 I **go to bed** / **get up** and I **have breakfast** / **have dinner**,
   At the start of every day.

2 I **go to sleep** / **go to school** and I **play** / **have lunch**,

3 I **work** / **play** and then I **work** / **play**.

4 I **have lunch** / **have dinner** with my **family** / **teacher**.

5 Then I have time to **swim** / **play**.

6 I **go to school** / **go to bed** and I **go to sleep** / **go to the park**.
   It's a busy, busy day!

DICTIONARY page D2

Lesson 6 — GRAMMAR

1 Read. Then look and check (✓).

I get up at seven o'clock. ✓

I go to sleep at seven o'clock. ○

I have breakfast at nine o'clock. ○

I have breakfast at ten o'clock. ○

I go to school at one o'clock. ○

I have lunch at one o'clock. ○

I go to sleep at eight o'clock. ○

I go to sleep at six o'clock. ○

2 Number the activities in the correct order for you. Then write.

a I have lunch at _____ o'clock. ○

b I go to sleep at _____ o'clock. ○

c I have breakfast at _____ o'clock. ○

d I go to school at _____ o'clock. ○

e I have dinner at _____ o'clock. ○

f I get up at _____ o'clock. ①

Lessons 7 and 8

LET'S VISIT GERMANY

1 Read and circle *True* or *False*.

1 Black Forest cake is from Germany. **True** / False
2 Black Forest cake is a traditional chocolate cake. True / False
3 Black Forest cake has chocolate and bananas. True / False
4 The boy eats cake in the morning. True / False

2 Now check your answers on page 26 of your Student's Book.

3 Complete the chart for your country.

Activity	Germany	My Country: _____
have breakfast	seven o'clock	_____ o'clock
go to school	eight o'clock	_____ o'clock
have lunch	one o'clock	_____ o'clock
have dinner	seven o'clock	_____ o'clock
go to sleep	eight o'clock	_____ o'clock

17

PLAY TIME

1 Read and connect the dots. Then write the letter.

1 shout … talk … sit down … stand up … clean up … talk

What's the letter? __p__

2 talk … shout … run … stand up … clean up

What's the letter? _____

3 shout … clean up … run … stand up … shout … talk … sit down

What's the letter? _____

4 stand up … talk … shout … sit down … stand up … run

What's the letter? _____

PLAY TIME

1 Look at the pictures and check (✓). Then write the secret question.

		1	2
a	It's eight o'clock.	✓ t	◯ k
b	It's five o'clock.	◯ p	◯ w
c	have breakfast	◯ o	◯ a
d	get up	◯ o	◯ p

		1	2
e	go to sleep	◯ s	◯ c
f	go to school	◯ l	◯ w
g	talk	◯ j	◯ o
h	have dinner	◯ r	◯ c
i	clean up	◯ k	◯ v

Is it ___ ___ ___ ___ ' ___ ___ ___ ___ ___ ___ ?

UNIT 3 — Lesson 1

·VOCABULARY·

1 Look and check (✓).

1. donkey ○
   duck ✓

2. chicken ○
   cow ○

3. goat ○
   duck ○

4. chicken ○
   sheep ○

5. sheep ○
   cow ○

6. chicken ○
   donkey ○

2 Look and write.

1 It's a ___chicken___.

2 It's a _____.

3 It's a _____.

4 It's a _____.

5 It's a _____.

6 It's a _____.

20

DICTIONARY page D3

Lesson 2

GRAMMAR

1 Look and connect.

1

This is ——— a duck.
That's

2

These are   cows.
Those are

3

This is   a goat.
That's

4

These are   chickens.
Those are

2 Read. Then circle and write.

1 This is a  . + This is a  .
= These are _____*goats*_____.

2 This is a . + This is a .
= These are _____.

3 That's a . + That's a .
= Those are _____.

Unit 3 — Lesson 3 — SPELLING

1 Read. Then underline *one* and *ose*.

2 Write *one* or *ose*.

1 Th___ ___ ___ are b___ ___ ___s.

2 Th___ ___ ___ are st___ ___ ___s.

3 Look at that n___ ___ ___!

Lesson 4

TAKE CARE OF A CLAY ANIMAL

Be responsible!

VALUES PROJECT

You need:
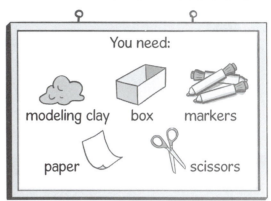
modeling clay, box, markers, paper, scissors

Make a clay farm animal.

Make a home for your animal.

Draw and cut out some food.

Take care of your animal.

About Me
What responsibilities do you have at school and at home?

23

Lesson 5

· VOCABULARY ·

1 Match the words and pictures.

1	ant	3	grasshopper	5	butterfly
2	mosquito	4	ladybug	6	caterpillar

a   b  c   d   e 1 f

2 Count and write.

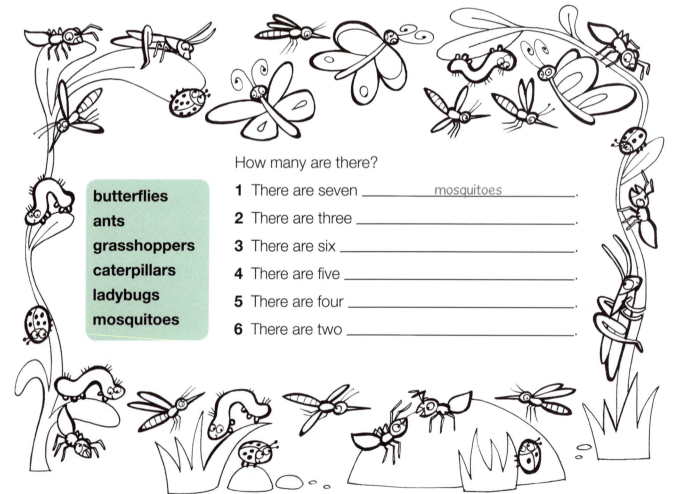

How many are there?

- butterflies
- ants
- grasshoppers
- caterpillars
- ladybugs
- mosquitoes

1 There are seven _____mosquitoes_____.
2 There are three _____.
3 There are six _____.
4 There are five _____.
5 There are four _____.
6 There are two _____.

DICTIONARY page D3

24

Lesson 6 · GRAMMAR ·

1 Look and write.

> It's a   They're   this   that   these   those

1 What's _____this_____?
_____It's a_____ ladybug.

2 What are _____?
_____ caterpillars.

3 What are _____?
_____ ants.

4 What's _____?
_____ grasshopper.

TRACK 29

2 Listen and connect.

What are these? What are these?
1 They're green grasshoppers.
What are those? What are those?
2 They're curly caterpillars.

What's that? What's that?
3 It's a shiny black cat.
And what's this? Ooh! Ouch! Stop! Oh, no!
4 It's an itchy, ouchy, itchy, ouchy mosquito!

a

b

c

d

Lessons 7 and 8

LET'S VISIT KENYA

1 Read. Then write and circle.

| flamingos | giraffes | zebras |

1 What are these? They're _____zebras_____.

2 Are they brown and gray?
Yes, they are. / No, they aren't.

3 What are these? They're _____.

4 Are they birds?
Yes, they are. / No, they aren't.

5 What are these? They're _____.

6 Do they have long necks?
Yes, they do. / No, they don't.

2 Color the spaces with a dot. Then circle and write.

What's this? / What are these?

It's a / They're giraffe. / zebras.

They're / It's from _____.

26

Lesson 1

· VOCABULARY ·

1 Find and circle the words. Then write.

potatoes

p	o	t	a	t	o	e	s
e	h	o	s	o	c	o	e
p	n	m	i	w	s	n	p
b	e	a	n	s	s	i	c
u	r	t	k	p	o	o	a
m	e	o	t	l	r	n	r
t	s	e	d	q	s	r
t	e	s	a	l	a	y	o
f	e	b	i	r	c	v	t
b	p	e	p	p	e	r	s

2 Look and write.

Those   These

1 These are potatoes_____.   4 _____.

2 Those_____.   5 _____.

3 _____.   6 _____.

DICTIONARY
page D4

27

Lesson 2

GRAMMAR

1 Write the questions. Then look and circle the answers.

1 Do you like bananas?

Do you like bananas ? Yes, I do. / No, I don't.

2 Do you like tomatoes?

_____? Yes, I do. / No, I don't.

3 Do you like beans?

_____? Yes, I do. / No, I don't.

4 Do you like apples?

_____? Yes, I do. / No, I don't.

2 Read and write the answers for you.   Yes, I do.   No, I don't.

1 Do you like peppers? _____.
2 Do you like beans? _____.
3 Do you like potatoes? _____.
4 Do you like onions? _____.
5 Do you like tomatoes? _____.
6 Do you like carrots? _____.

Lesson 3

1 Read. Then underline *une* and *oon*.

2 Write *une* or *oon*.

1 Good aftern___ ___ ___, Miss M___ ___ ___.

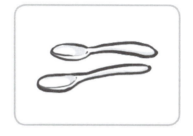

2 They're sp___ ___ ___s.

3 Do you like my t___ ___ ___, Miss M___ ___ ___?

29

Lesson 4

MAKE A NEW THINGS POSTER

Try new things!

VALUES PROJECT

You need: magazines, paper, marker, scissors, glue, pencils

Choose the foods you want to try.

Write: **New things to try this week.**

Draw or glue pictures of the foods you want to try.

Take the poster home.

Mmm ... delicious!

About Me
Why is it good to try new things?

30

Lesson 5

VOCABULARY

1 Circle the missing letter. Then write.

1 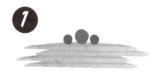 ⓐ/ i

p_a_nc_a_kes

2  e / a

Fr___nch fri___s

3  t / r

hambu___ge___s

4  s / t

___andwiche___

5  p / c

ice ___o___s

6  o / e

c___ ___kies

2 Look at Activity 1. Write the snacks in the order that you like them.

☺ 1 _____
   2 _____
   3 _____
   4 _____
   5 _____
☹ 6 _____

DICTIONARY
page D4

31

UNIT 4

Lesson 6

GRAMMAR

1 Look and write.

I like   I don't like

① _____ carrots.

② _____ pancakes.

③ _____ ice pops.

④ _____ hamburgers.

TRACK 37

2 Listen and write. Then connect.

1 Do you like h_a_ _m_ _b_ _u_r_ _ _ _ge_r_ _ _s_?

2 Do you like ___ ___n___ ___ ___s?

3 Do you like everything?

a No, I don't. No, I don't. I don't like spiders and I don't like snakes!

b Yes, I do. Yes, I do. I like ___ ___ ___b___r___ ___ ___ ___ with ___ ___io___ ___.

c Yes, I do. Yes, I do. I like ___a___a___ ___ ___ with hot p___ ___c___ ___ ___ ___.

Lessons 7 and 8

LET'S VISIT TURKEY

1 Match the questions and answers.

1 What's Turkish delight? ○
2 Is Ahmet's dad a teacher? ○
3 Does he have pancakes on his stand? ○
4 Does he have peppers? ○

a No, he isn't.
b No, he doesn't.
c Yes, he does.
d It's a candy.

2 Now check your answers on page 50 of your Student's Book.

3 Draw vegetables from your country. Then write.

potatoes	carrots
peppers	onions
beans	tomatoes
I like	I don't like
These are	

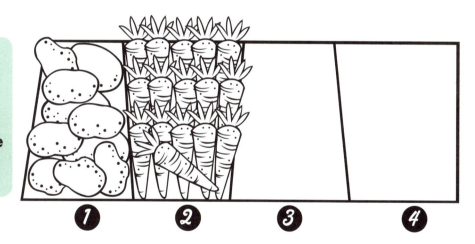

❶   ❷   ❸   ❹

1 These are potatoes   . I like potatoes   .
2 _____. _____.
3 _____. _____.
4 _____. _____.

33

PLAY TIME

1 Complete the puzzles.

Puzzle a

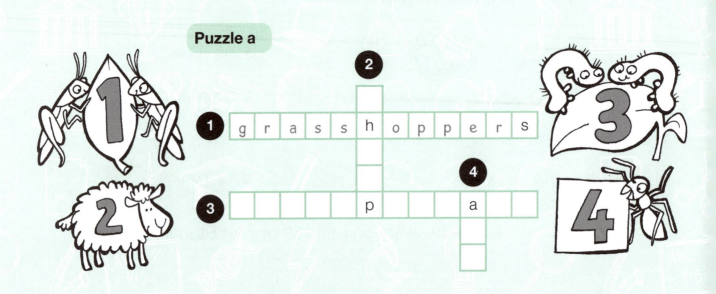

Puzzle b

PLAY TIME

1 Look and check (✓) the things in the picture.

potatoes ✓	peppers ○	carrots ○	sandwiches ○
ice pops ○	pancakes ○	chickens ○	cows ○
ducks ○	onions ○	goats ○	tomatoes ○

2 Look at Activity 1. Complete the chart for you.

I like ... 🙂	I don't like ... ☹
potatoes	

35

Lesson 1

1 Match the words and pictures. Then write.

1 climb a tree   3 play the guitar   5 touch your toes
2 speak Vietnamese   4 do taekwondo   6 jump rope

_____   _____   _____

_____   climb a tree   _____

2 Write and color the correct squares to complete the chart.

	a	b	c	d	e	f
	Vietnamese	the guitar	rope	_____	taekwondo	your toes
1	do						
2	climb						
3	jump						
4	_____						
5	touch						
6	_____						

DICTIONARY page D5

Lesson 2

GRAMMAR

1 Read. Then look and write.

Yes, I can.   No, I can't.

1 Can you touch your toes?

2 Can you climb a tree?

3 Can you play the guitar?

4 Can you jump rope?

2 Complete the questions. Then check (✓) for you.

                                             Yes, I can.   No, I can't.

1 _____Can you_____ touch your toes?   ○   ○

2 _____ speak Vietnamese?   ○   ○

3 _____ play the guitar?   ○   ○

4 _____ climb a tree?   ○   ○

37

Lesson 3

SPELLING

1 Read. Then underline _ea_ and _ee_.

In the morning, I go to school. I like my teacher.

I have lunch under a tree.

I go home at three o'clock in the afternoon.

2 Write _ea_ or _ee_.

1 I like my t___ ___cher.
"Rep___ ___t after me."

2 I have lunch under a tr___ ___.

3 I go home at thr___ ___ o'clock.

Lesson 4

MAKE AN *I CAN* COLLAGE

Be positive!

VALUES PROJECT

You need:
- magazines
- paper
- marker
- scissors
- glue

Cut out pictures of things you can do.

Write: **Things I can do**.

Glue your pictures. Display the collage on the wall.

Ask a friend: **What can you do?**

I can jump rope.

About Me
What can you do without asking adults for help?

39

Lesson 5

· VOCABULARY ·

1 Circle the words and write. Then connect.

1 lkwalkakl = _w_ _a_ _l_ _k_
2 hpohophp = ___ ___ ___
3 misswimi = ___ ___ ___ ___
4 deridedir a orhhorsese =
___ ___ ___ ___ ___ ___ ___ ___ ___
5 lyffly = ___ ___ ___
6 ngssingisg = ___ ___ ___ ___

2 Read. Then look and write.

Yes, I can.   No, I can't.

1 Can you fly? — Yes, I can.
2 Can you hop?
3 Can you walk?
4 Can you climb?

40 DICTIONARY page D5

Lesson 6

GRAMMAR

1 Read and circle *True* or *False*. Correct the false sentences.

1

Goats can't run.   True / (False)

Goats can run _____.

2

Chickens can't swim.   True / False

_____.

3

Cows can hop.   True / False

_____.

4

Sheep can walk.   True / False

_____.

TRACK 46

2 Listen, read, and connect in the correct order.

I can speak Vietnamese,	But I can't, no, I can't,	I just can't fly!
I can do taekwondo.	I can swim, I can hop,	I can jump up high.
I can touch my big toe.	I can play the guitar,	

41

Lessons 7 and 8

LET'S VISIT SOUTH KOREA

1 Write the words. Then complete the answer.

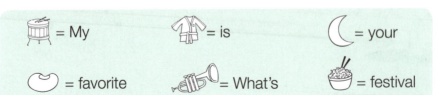

___What's___ _____ _____ _____?

_____ _____ _____ _____.

2 Read and write the answers.

Yes, they can.   No, they can't.

At your favorite festival ...

1 can people dance? _____.
2 can they play the guitar? _____.
3 can they wrestle? _____.
4 can they eat special food? _____.
5 can they sing traditional songs? _____.

Unit 6

Lesson 1 · VOCABULARY ·

1 Connect the pictures. Then write.

1 <u>play soccer</u>
2 _____
3 _____
4 _____
5 _____
6 _____

2 Write sentences for you.

1 play / don't play   I _____ board games every day.
2 sing / don't sing   I _____ karaoke every day.
3 play / don't play   I _____ soccer every day.
4 read / don't read   I _____ books every day.
5 watch / don't watch   I _____ TV every day.
6 play / don't play   I _____ computer games every day.

DICTIONARY page D6

43

Lesson 2

GRAMMAR

1 Unscramble the words.

 1 reading I books like

I like reading books.

 2 like I computer don't playing games

_____.

 3 soccer like don't I playing

_____.

 4 karaoke like singing I

_____.

2 Read. Then look and write for you.

I like   I don't like

What do you like doing?

1 _____ playing _____soccer_____.

2 _____ watching _____.

 3 _____ jumping _____.

4 _____ playing the _____.

 5 _____ speaking _____.

44

Lesson 3

1 Read. Then underline *ai* and *ay*.

2 Write *ai* or *ay*.

1 It's r___ ___ny tod___ ___.
Come and pl___ ___!

2 I don't like r___ ___ny d___ ___s.

3 I like pl___ ___ing with my tr___ ___n.

Lesson 4

MAKE A FRIENDSHIP BRACELET

Value your friends!

VALUES PROJECT

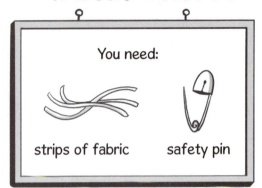

You need: strips of fabric, safety pin

Tie three strips of fabric in a knot at one end.

Pin the fabric strips to your pants and braid them.

Tie a knot in the other end.

Exchange bracelets with a friend.

About Me
What special things do you do for your friends?

Lesson 5 ·VOCABULARY·

1 Match the words and pictures. Then write.

1 listen to music   3 draw   5 dance
2 paint   4 do puzzles   6 make models

listen to music

2 Look and circle *True* or *False*. Correct the false sentences.

1 I like listening to music.   True / **False**   I like painting.
2 I like painting.   True / False   _____.
3 I like making models.   True / False   _____.
4 I like dancing.   True / False   _____.

DICTIONARY page D6

47

Lesson 6 · GRAMMAR ·

1 Look and connect.

1 She likes ——— listening to music.
   She doesn't like

2 He likes ——— playing soccer.
   He doesn't like

3 She likes ——— swimming.
   She doesn't like

4 He likes ——— reading.
   He doesn't like

TRACK 56

2 Listen and circle.

1 He likes **playing soccer at school.** / **(reading books at school.)**

2 She likes **swimming in the pool.** / **reading books at school.**

*But they both like playing with friends.
They both like playing with friends.*

3 She doesn't like **climbing a tree.** / **speaking Vietnamese.**

4 He doesn't like **climbing a tree.** / **watching TV.**

Lessons 7 and 8

LET'S VISIT ARGENTINA

1 Write.

> listening   watching   dancing   playing

Roberto likes **1** _____playing_____ soccer with his friends and he likes

2 _____ soccer on TV.

His grandma doesn't like playing soccer!

She likes **3** _____ to music

and **4** _____.

Her favorite dance is the tango.

2 Now check your answers on page 74 of your Student's Book.

3 Read and write the answers.

> Yes, they do.   No, they don't.

Do people in your country …

1 like watching soccer on TV? _____.
2 like dancing the tango? _____.
3 like listening to music? _____.
4 like playing soccer? _____.
5 like wrestling? _____.
6 like doing taekwondo? _____.

49

PLAY TIME

1 Look at the pictures and check (✓).
Then write the secret question.

	1	2
a touch their toes	✓ s	○ x
b fly kites	○ v	○ p
c jump rope	○ e	○ y
d hop	○ a	○ o
e ride a horse	○ j	○ k
f climb a tree	○ R	○ E

	1	2
g sing	○ n	○ p
h walk	○ q	○ g
i dance	○ l	○ m
j play the guitar	○ i	○ e
k swim	○ g	○ s
l do taekwondo	○ z	○ h

Can you s _ _ _ _ _ _ _ _ _ _ _ _ ?

50

PLAY TIME

1 Find and circle the words.

puzzles   models   soccer   TV   karaoke
computer games   books   board games

s	e	b	o	a	r	d	g	a	m	e	s	p	m	v
o	h	b	o	o	k	s	q	o	t	v	a	i	y	v
c	n	i	m	o	d	e	l	s	p	u	a	s	l	y
c	h	a	m	e	k	p	u	z	z	l	e	s	o	z
e	r	c	o	m	p	u	t	e	r	g	a	m	e	s
r	k	a	r	a	o	k	e	u	p	m	o	c	p	o

2 Play a miming game. Throw a coin onto a space. Mime the action for a friend to guess.

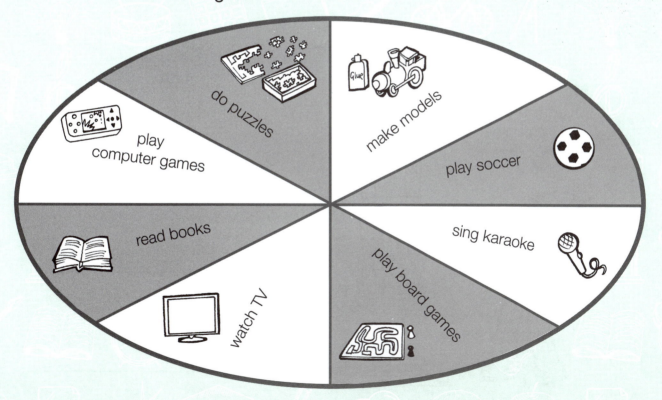

UNIT 7

Lesson 1

·VOCABULARY·

1 Write. Then look and circle.

a p a r t m e n t   __ __ __ i __ e __

c__ __ __ le   __ __ v __

b__ __ __   __ o __ s __

2 Look and write.

1 This is my _____.

2 _____.

3 _____.

52   DICTIONARY page D7

Lesson 2

1 Read and follow the paths.

1 She lives in a trailer.   **2** It lives in a house.   **3** He lives in a boat.

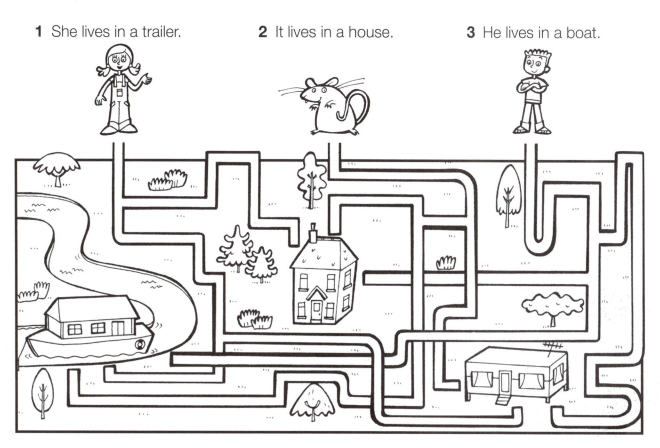

2 Circle. Then draw and write.

1 He / She   castle / trailer   **2** He / She   boat / house

_____ lives in a _____.   _____.

UNIT 7   Lesson 3   · SPELLING ·

1 Read. Then underline *igh*, *y*, and *ie*.

2 Write *igh*, *y*, or *ie*.

1 Mmm … Apple p___ ___!

2 This p___ ___ can fl___ h___ ___ ___ in the sk___!

3 Stop! That's m___ p___ ___.

Lesson 4

MAKE A *WELCOME* SIGN

Welcome people!

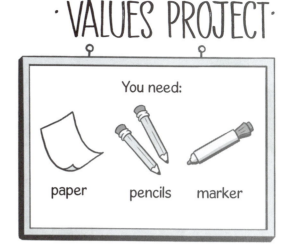

VALUES PROJECT

You need: paper, pencils, marker

Write: **Welcome to my _____!**

Draw your house.

Hang the poster in your house.

Write visitors' names on your sign.

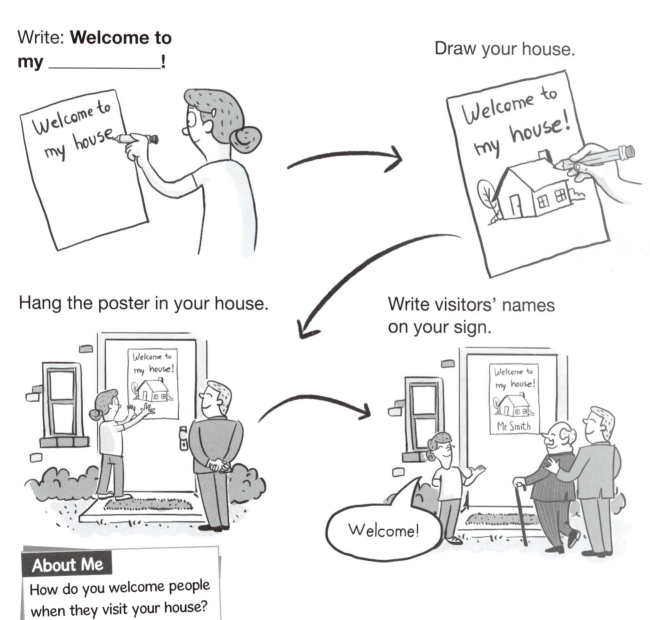

About Me
How do you welcome people when they visit your house?

Lesson 5

VOCABULARY

1 Look and write.

jungle   city   country   ocean   woods   desert

1 ____desert____   4 _____

2 _____   5 _____

3 _____   6 _____

2 Look and circle.

 1 It lives in the **desert**. / **city**.

2 It lives in the **city**. / **jungle**.

 3 It lives in the **country**. / **ocean**.

4 It lives in the **ocean**. / **woods**.

DICTIONARY page D7

56

Lesson 6

GRAMMAR

1 Read. Then look and write.

1 Where do you live?

I live in the country.

2 Where do you live?

3 Where do you live?

4 Where do you live?

TRACK 65

2 Listen and write. Then check (✓).

1 Where do you live ?

   I live in the _____ desert _____.

   The _____! The _____!

   The sizzling fizzling _____!

2 _____?

   I live in the _____.

   The _____! The _____!

   The splishy splashy _____!

3 _____?

   I live in the _____.

   The _____! The _____!

   The busy whizzy _____!

57

Lessons 7 and 8

LET'S VISIT MONGOLIA

1 Match the pieces to the puzzle. Then read and check (✓) the correct sentences.

Puzzle 1

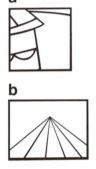

Puzzle 2

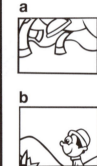

1 In Mongolia, lots of people live in castles. ○

2 In Mongolia, lots of people live in tents. ✓

3 In Mongolia, people ride horses. ○

4 In Mongolia, people ride camels. ○

2 Read and write the answers for you.

| Yes, I do. | No, I don't. | Yes, I can. | No, I can't. |

1 Do you live in a yurt? _____.

2 Do you live in an apartment? _____.

3 Do you live in a house? _____.

4 Do you like horses? _____.

5 Can you ride a horse? _____.

6 Can you ride a bike? _____.

Lesson 1 · VOCABULARY·

1 Look and write.

> violin   recorder   piano   drums   trumpet   tambourine

1. tambourine
2. _____
3. _____
4. _____
5. _____
6. _____

2 Circle the words. Then write the words in the correct column for you.

I can play the …	I can't play the …

DICTIONARY page D8

59

Lesson 2

GRAMMAR

1 Look. Then read and check (✓).

Yes, I do.   No, I don't.

1 Do you play the tambourine? ✓ ◯
2 Do you play the piano? ◯ ◯
3 Do you play the drums? ◯ ◯
4 Do you play the trumpet? ◯ ◯
5 Do you play the violin? ◯ ◯

2 Complete the questions. Then write the answers for you.

1 __Do__ __you__ play computer games? _____.
2 _____ _____ play soccer? _____.
3 _____ _____ play the piano? _____.
4 _____ _____ play the trumpet? _____.
5 _____ _____ play board games? _____.
6 _____ _____ play with dolls? _____.
7 _____ _____ play with robots? _____.

Lesson 3 · SPELLING·

1 Read and color. Then underline *oa* and *ow*.

Milly the goat has a yellow boat.

Milly the goat has a yellow coat.

Milly rows her yellow boat in her yellow coat!

2 Write *oa* or *ow*.

1 Milly the g___ ___t has a yell___ ___ b___ ___t.

2 Milly the goat has a yell___ ___ c___ ___t.

3 Milly r___ ___s her yell___ ___ b___ ___t.

61

Lesson 4

MAKE A PROMISE CARD

Help your friends!

VALUES PROJECT

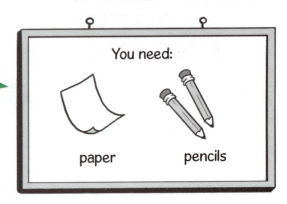

You need:
paper   pencils

Write your name. Then write **I play** _____.

Find someone to help.

"Do you play the recorder?"

"No, I don't."

Make a promise card.

Help your friend!

About Me
How do you help your friends at school?

Lesson 5 · VOCABULARY ·

1 Connect in the correct order.

Sunday   Thursday   Saturday   Wednesday   Friday   Monday   Tuesday

2 Write the days. Then complete the diary for you.

I ...
go to school
go to the park
go to the mall
sing
do puzzles
draw
read books
watch TV
listen to music

1 S_u_ _n_day   _____
2 M___nd___y   ___I go to school.___
3 T___ ___sday   _____
4 Wed___ ___ ___day   _____
5 Th___ ___ ___day   _____
6 Fr___da___   _____
7 S___t___rd___y   _____

3 Look at Activity 2 and write the answers.

Yes, I do.   No, I don't.

1 Do you go to school on Sundays? _____.
2 Do you draw on Wednesdays? _____.
3 Do you watch TV on Tuesdays? _____.

DICTIONARY page D8

63

Lesson 6

GRAMMAR

1 Look. Then read and write.

Yes, he does.   No, he doesn't.

Monday

Tuesday

Wednesday

Thursday

Friday

Saturday

Sunday

1 Does he read books on Mondays? _____No, he doesn't_____.

2 Does he play computer games on Tuesdays? _____.

3 Does he ride his bike on Thursdays? _____.

4 Does he play the violin on Fridays? _____.

5 Does he play the piano on Saturdays? _____.

6 Does he paint on Sundays? _____.

TRACK 76

2 Listen and complete the chart for the girl in the song.

Day	Activity
Monday	**1** play soccer
Tuesday	2
Wednesday	3
Thursday	4
Friday	5

Lessons 7 and 8

LET'S VISIT AUSTRALIA

1 Look at page 98 of your Student's Book. Circle the mistakes in Bahloo's planner. Then write the correct activities.

DAY	ACTIVITY	ACTIVITY
Monday	(draw pictures)	play music
Tuesday	play music	
Wednesday	play music	
Thursday	draw pictures	
Friday	play computer games	
Saturday	make models and sing	
Sunday	make models and paint	

2 Use the key to color the picture. Then circle the correct answer.

1 = orange   2 = blue   3 = yellow

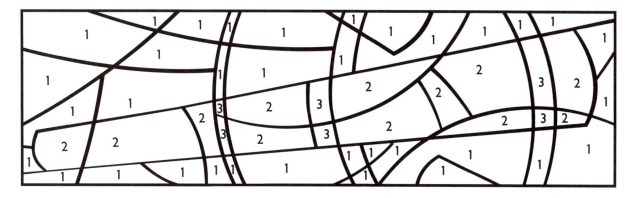

This is a **trumpet**. / **didgeridoo**.

65

PLAY TIME

1 Complete the puzzle. Then use the extra word to complete Bubba's sentence.

PLAY TIME

1 Write the number and draw. Then read and write.

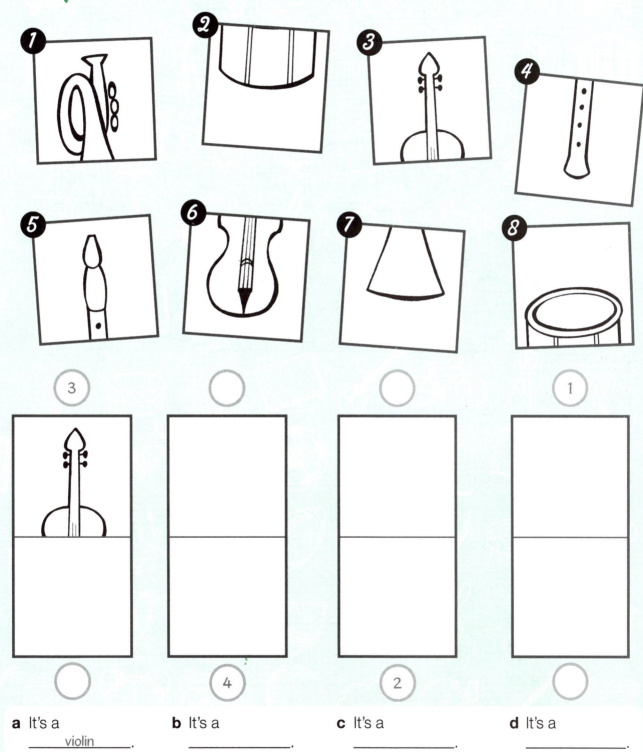

a It's a
___violin___.

b It's a
_____.

c It's a
_____.

d It's a
_____.

Unit 9

Lesson 1

VOCABULARY

1 Match the sentences to the picture. Then color.

1 There's a red bus.   e
2 There's a blue car.
3 There's a green helicopter.

4 There's an orange train.
5 There's a white airplane.
6 There's a gray motorcycle.

2 Find and write.

1 prehcleito   helicopter
2 tirna   _____
3 ubs   _____
4 rotcoemycl   _____
5 rca   _____
6 paarlein   _____

DICTIONARY
page D9

68

Lesson 2 · GRAMMAR ·

1 Read and match. Then circle the pictures using the correct color.

1 = red   2 = yellow   3 = blue   4 = green   5 = purple   6 = brown

1 He doesn't go to the mall by car.
2 She goes to the movie theater by bus.
3 She doesn't go to the beach by helicopter.
4 She doesn't go to school by bike.
5 He goes to school by bike.
6 He goes to the mountains by train.

2 Write.

1 Igotoschoolbycar.   I go to school by car   .

2 Idon'tgotoschoolbybus.   _____.

3 Hegoestoschoolbytrain.   _____.

4 Shedoesn'tgotoschoolbybike.   _____.

69

Unit 9 Lesson 3 · SPELLING ·

1 Read. Then underline *ue* and *ew*.

Sue has new blue shoes.

2 Write *ue* or *ew*.

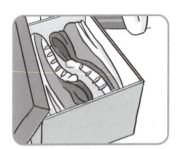

1 Sue has n___ ___ bl___ ___ shoes.

2 I don't like the bl___ ___ shoes.

3 A box and some gl___ ___. A n___ ___ house for my doll!

Lesson 4

MAKE A DISPLAY

Care for the environment!

VALUES PROJECT

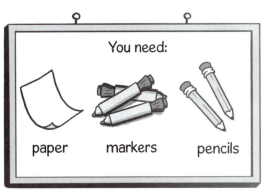

Draw pictures of the environment.

Draw pictures of vehicles that are bad for the environment.

Draw pictures of vehicles that are good for the environment.

Make a class display.

About Me
What can you do to care for the environment?

Lesson 5

1 Read. Then write the numbers.

a ___100___   e _____   i _____
  one hundred   fifty   ninety

b _____   f _____   j _____
  forty   eighty   thirty

c _____   g _____
  sixty   ten

d _____   h _____
  twenty   seventy

2 Read. Then solve and write.

1 _____Thirty_____ and ten is forty.
2 _____ and twenty is seventy.
3 _____ and fifty is eighty.
4 _____ and thirty is ninety.
5 _____ and ten is one hundred.

3 Read and connect the dots. Then write.

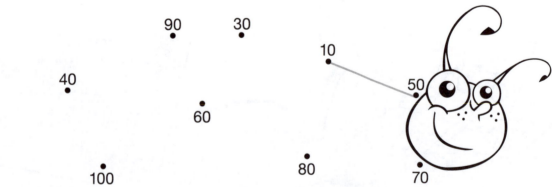

fifty … ten … thirty … ninety … forty … twenty … one hundred … sixty … eighty … seventy.

It's a _____.

Lesson 6

GRAMMAR

1 Complete the questions. Then write the answers for you.

1 How many books are there in your backpack?

There are _____.

2 _____ pencils are there in your pencil case?

_____.

3 _____ pens are there in your pencil case?

_____.

4 _____ children are there in your classroom?

_____.

5 _____ chairs are there in your classroom?

_____.

6 _____ pages are there in this book?

_____.

TRACK 85

2 Listen and circle. Then write.

How many apples are there in the picnic box?

1 There are (**forty**) / **fifty** and **twelve**, / (**two**),

That makes _____forty-two_____ …

How many sandwiches are there in the picnic box?

2 There are **twelve** / **twenty** and **six**, / **seven**,

That makes _____ …

How many cookies are there in the picnic box?

3 There are **thirty** / **fifty** and **three**, / **five**,

That makes _____ …

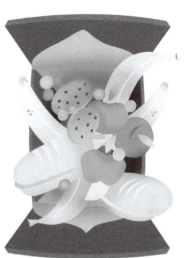

73

Unit 9 — Lessons 7 and 8

LET'S VISIT THAILAND

1 Check (✓) the true sentences. Then write a postcard.

1 Bangkok is in Thailand. ◯
2 There are lots of cars and buses. ◯
3 There are castles. ◯
4 Some people go to work by river taxi. ◯

Dear _____,

I'm in Bangkok!

Bangkok is in Thailand.

_____

_____

From _____

_____

12 Washington Street

New York

USA

2 Write the words. Then draw for you.

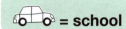 = school   = go   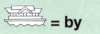 = by   = to   = I

I _____ _____ _____ _____ _____

Unit 10 Lesson 1

VOCABULARY

1 Unscramble the words to make sentences. Then match the sentences to the picture and color.

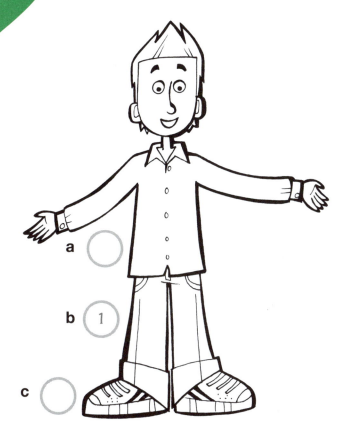

1 gray They're pants — They're gray pants.
2 sneakers They're blue — _____.
3 a red shirt It's — _____.
4 skirt It's pink a — _____.
5 a It's green sweater — _____.
6 orange They're shoes — _____.

2 Unscramble the letters and write the words.

1 sseoh _____   3 tksri _____
2 saeerkns _____ 4 tpnsa _____

UNIT 10

Lesson 2

GRAMMAR

1 Look and write.

shoes
backpack
pants
hat
sweater

 1 These are _____Hannah's pants_____.

 2 This is _____.

 3 This is _____.

 4 This is _____.

 5 These are _____.

2 Look at Activity 1. Draw and write.

1 _____ Ben's _____.

2 _____ Hannah's _____.

76

Lesson 3 · SPELLING·

1 Read. Then underline *th* in red or in blue.

2 Write *th* in red or in blue.

1 ___ ___is is my family. Do you like our clo___ ___es?

2 This is my mo___ ___er and this is my fa___ ___er.

3 And ___ ___ese are my ___ ___ree bro___ ___ers.

77

UNIT 10 — Lesson 4

MAKE A SHARING TOKEN

Share with family and friends!

VALUES PROJECT

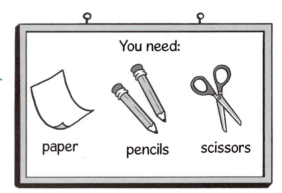

You need: paper, pencils, scissors

Draw a circle.

Draw your favorite toy.

Write: **You can share my** _____.
Cut out the circle.

Give the sharing token to someone in your family.

"You can share my airplane today."

"Thank you!"

About Me
What do you share with your friends at school?

Lesson 5

VOCABULARY

1 Look and check (✓).

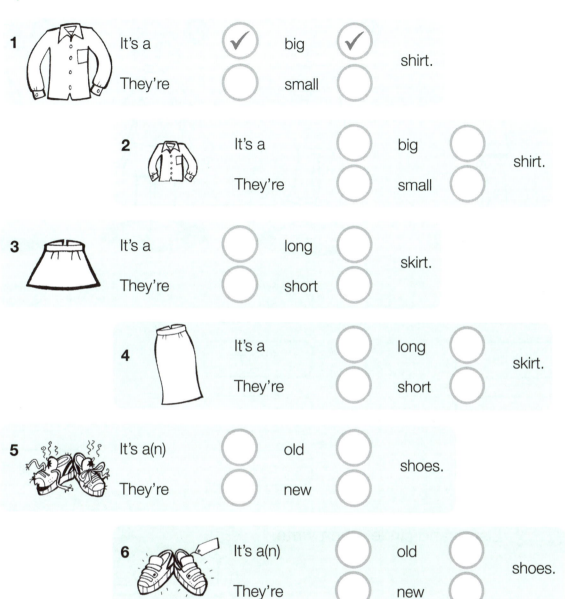

2 Look and write.

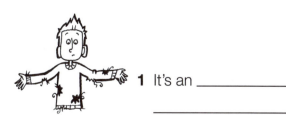

1 It's an _____ _____.

2 They're _____ _____.

DICTIONARY page D10

Lesson 6

GRAMMAR

1 Look and connect.

1	He has	short	sweater.
2	She has	a long	pants.
3	He has	a small	hat.
4	She has	a big	skirt.

TRACK 93

2 Listen and circle. Then write.

1 (new) / old   (shirt) / skirt   I have a ____new____ ____shirt____.
2 new / old   shirt / skirt   She has an _____ _____.
3 small / big   sneakers / shoes   He has _____ _____.
4 small / big   sneakers / shoes   I have _____ _____.

80

Lessons 7 and 8

LET'S VISIT PERU

1 Read and circle *True* or *False*.

1 Pan pipes are short and long.   True / False
2 Guitars from Peru are big.   True / False
3 Pan pipes are from South Korea.   True / False

2 Now check your answers on page 122 of your Student's Book.

3 Read and color. Then write the answers for you.

Rosa has a big, black hat. She has a long, black and red skirt.

1 Do you have a black hat?
_____.

2 Do you have a long skirt?
_____.

Xavi has a small, brown hat. He has old, blue pants.

3 Do you have a brown hat?
_____.

4 Do you have blue pants?
_____.

PLAY TIME

1 Add and write the number. Then complete the puzzle.

a 22 + 17 = __39__ =

b 13 + 48 = _____ =

c 82 + 11 = _____ =

d 17 + 17 = _____ =

e 25 + 27 = _____ =

f 51 + 25 = _____ =

g 22 + 26 = _____ =

39 — m o t o r c y c l e

61 — r . . i . . .

48 — . . . . p . . e

34 — b . e

82

PLAY TIME

1 Look and check (✓) the things in the picture.

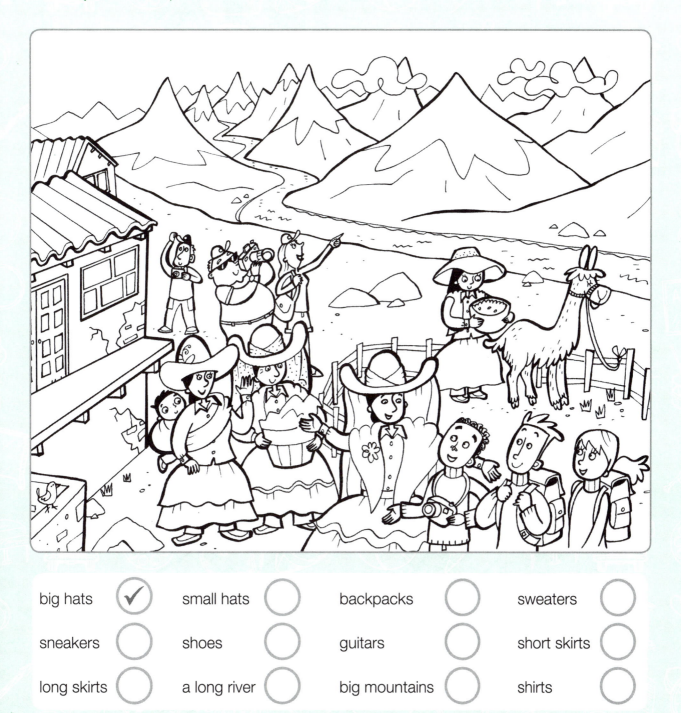

big hats	✓	small hats	○	backpacks	○	sweaters	○
sneakers	○	shoes	○	guitars	○	short skirts	○
long skirts	○	a long river	○	big mountains	○	shirts	○

83

MY DICTIONARY

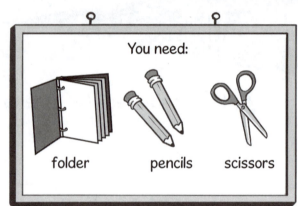

How to Make Your Dictionary

Open your *Next Station* Workbook at the *My Dictionary* section.

Complete the *My Dictionary* pages for the unit.

Cut out the *My Dictionary* pages after all the units are completed.

Keep the pages in a folder and label it *My Dictionary*. Use it to review your *Next Station* vocabulary!

84

MY DICTIONARY

Page 4 Look and write.

_____   _____   _____

_____   _____   _____

Page 8 Number the items in alphabetical order.

A B C D E F G H I J K L M
N O P Q R S T U V W X Y Z

elephant ○   desk ○   rabbit ○   farmer ○   mouth ○

zoo ○   lake ○   watermelon ○   apple (1)   bedroom ○

D1

· MY DICTIONARY ·

Page 11 Look and write.

      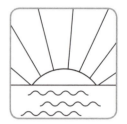

_____   _____   _____

_____   _____   _____

Page 15 Write the activities in the order you do them. Then connect.

1 ____get up____

2 _____

3 _____

4 _____

5 _____

6 _____

MY DICTIONARY

Page 20 Write and draw.

_____   _____   _____

      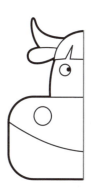

_____   _____   _____

Page 24 Look and circle.

ladybug   grasshopper

caterpillar   butterfly

ant   mosquito

D3

MY DICTIONARY

Page 27 Read and draw.

potatoes	beans	onions
peppers	tomatoes	carrots

Page 31 Write. Then use the color key to circle the words in alphabetical order.

1 = red   2 = yellow   3 = blue   4 = green   5 = pink   6 = brown

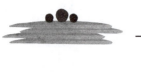 ____ancakes

 ____andwiches

 ____rench fries

 ____ce pops

 ____amburgers

 ____ookies

D4

MY DICTIONARY

Page 36   Write. Then connect.

cl___m___ a tr___ ___   sp___ ___ ___ Vietn___ ___ese

___ ___ay the g___ ___tar   ___o t___ekw___n___o

t___ ___ch yo___ ___ ___oes   j___ ___p ___ ___pe

Page 40   Connect the letters. Then write and match.

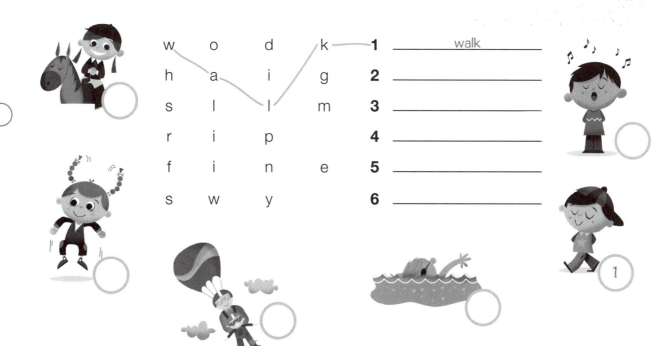

```
w   o   d   k     1 ____walk____
h   a   i   g     2 _____
s   l   l   m     3 _____
r   i   p         4 _____
f   i   n   e     5 _____
s   w   y         6 _____
```

MY DICTIONARY

Page 43 Draw the missing objects. Then write.

_____ _____ _____

_____ _____ _____

Page 47 Cross out (✗) the one that's different. Then write.

1   _listen to music_

2   _____

3   _____

4   _____

5   _____

6   _____

MY DICTIONARY

Page 52 Read and draw.

castle

house

trailer

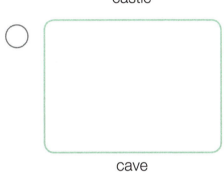
cave

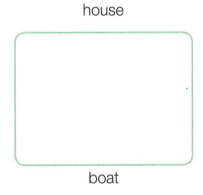
boat

apartment

Page 56 Write. Then connect.

c___ ___ ___

___ ___ ___ ___le

w___ ___ ___ ___

___oun___ ___ ___

___ ___ ___ ___rt

___c___ ___ ___

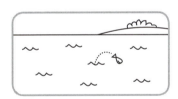

MY DICTIONARY

Page 59 Draw and write.

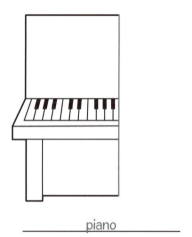

piano

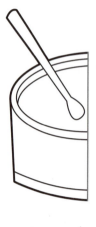

drum

tambourine

_____ _____

_____ _____

_____ _____

Page 63 Find and write.

1 yauSnd _____

2 nodMay _____

3 dTuasye _____

4 yeesaWddn _____

5 dhTsauyr _____

6 ardiyF _____

7 aaStudry _____

MY DICTIONARY

Page 68 Read and draw.

motorcycle	bus	train

helicopter	car	airplane

Page 72 Look and write.

20   **30**   **40**   **50**

___ ___ ___nty   ___ ___ ___ty   f___ ___ty   ___i___ty

60   **70**   **80**

six___ ___   s___v___n___ ___   e___ ___h___ ___

90   **100**

n___ ___e___ ___   one ___ ___ ___ ___ ___ ___ ___

D9

MY DICTIONARY

Page 75 Look and write.

_____   _____

_____   _____

_____   _____

Page 79 Connect the opposites. Then write.

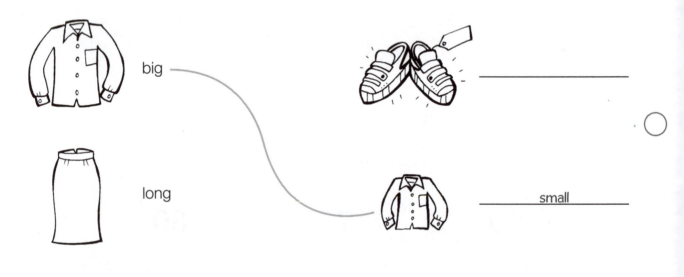

big

long

   _____

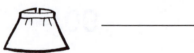   _____small_____

old   _____

NEXT STATION LEVEL 2 | PROGRESS RECORD

Read and circle.

 Country: **Canada** / **Peru**
Don't stand **down**. / **up**. Please, sit **down**. / **up**.

 Country: **Mongolia** / **Germany**
I get up at eight o'clock **in the morning**. / **at night**.

 Country: **South Korea** / **Kenya**
What are **this**? / **those**? **It's** / **They're** ladybugs.

 Country: **Thailand** / **Turkey**
Do you like sandwiches? Yes, I **do**. / **don't**.

 Country: **South Korea** / **Kenya**
I can speak English but I **can** / **can't** fly.

 Country: **Argentina** / **Australia**
I **like** / **likes** singing but he doesn't **like** / **likes** dancing.

 Country: **Germany** / **Mongolia**
I **live** / **lives** in the city. She **live** / **lives** in the country.

 Country: **Argentina** / **Australia**
Do / **Does** he play the drums? No, he **does**. / **doesn't**.

 Country: **Thailand** / **Turkey**
How many **pen** / **pens** are there? There are **one**. / **three**.

 Country: **Peru** / **Canada**
This / **These** are Maria's shoes.

Next Station ... Level 3!

2020 © Macmillan Education do Brasil

Based on *Next Move*
© Macmillan Publishers Limited 2013
Text © Cantabgilly Limited and Mary Charrington 2013
Adapted by Viv Lambert
Next Move is a registered trademark, property of Macmillan Publishers, 2013
First edition entitled "Next Stop" published 2009 by Macmillan Publishers

Director of Languages Brazil: Patrícia Souza De Luccia
Publishing Manager and Field Researcher: Patricia Muradas
Content Creation Coordinator: Cristina do Vale
Art Editor: Jean Aranha
Lead Editors: Ana Beatriz da Costa Moreira, Daniela Gonçala da Costa, Luciana Pereira da Silva
Content Editors: Millyane M. Moura Moreira, Tarsílio Soares Moreira
Digital Editor: Ana Paula Girardi
Editorial Assistant: Roberta Somera
Editorial Intern: Bruna Marques
Art Assistant: Denis Araujo
Art Intern: Jacqueline Alves
Graphic Production: Tatiane Romano, Thais Mendes P. Galvão
Proofreaders: Edward Willson, Márcia Leme, Sabrina Cairo Bileski
Design Concept: Design Divertido Artes Gráficas
Page Make-Up: Figurattiva Editorial
Image Processing: Jean Aranha, Jacqueline Alves, Denis Araujo
Audio: Argila Music, Núcleo de Criação
Cover Concept: Jean Aranha
Cover photography: TommL/iStockphoto/Getty Images, Bubert/iStockphoto/Getty Images, LokFung/iStockphoto/Getty Images.
Illustrations: Gustavo Gialuca (p. 6, 7, 13, 14, 22, 23, 29, 30, 38, 39, 45, 46, 54, 55, 61, 62, 70, 71, 77, 78, 84), John Haslam (p. 59, D1, D2, D3, D6, D8), Andrew Painter | Lemonade Illustration (p. 8, 10, 16, 17, 19, 26, 27, 33, 42, 49, 50, 58, 65, 74, 81), Jim Peacock | Beehive Illustration (p. 4, 5, 10, 12, 15, 18, 21, 24, 25, 26, 31, 33, 36, 37, 41, 42, 44, 47, 48, 50, 56, 58, 66, 69, 72, 74, 76, 80, 81, 95), Melanie Sharpe | Sylvie Poggio Artists Agency (p. 4, 9, 11, 19, 20, 24, 28, 32, 33, 34, 35, 40, 43, 47, 48, 51, 52, 53, 56, 57, 59, 60, 64, 67, 68, 73, 75, 79, 82, 83, D6, D7, 95).

Reproduction prohibited. Penal Code Article 184 and Law number 9.610 of February 19, 1998.

We would like to dedicate this book to teachers all over Brazil. We would also like to thank our clients and teachers who have helped us make this book better with their many rich contributions and feedback straight from the classroom!

Dados Internacionais de Catalogação na Publicação (CIP)
Bibliotecária responsável: Aline Graziele Benitez CRB-1/3129

C23n	Cant, Amanda
1.ed.	Next Station 2: Workbook / Amanda Cant; [Adapt.] Viv Lambert. – 1.ed. – São Paulo: Macmillan Education do Brasil, 2020.
	96 p.; il.; 21 x 27 cm. – (Coleção Next Station)
	ISBN: 978-85-511-0138-4
	1. Língua inglesa. I. Lambert, Viv. II. Título. III. Série. CDD 420

Índice para catálogo sistemático:
1. Língua inglesa

All rights reserved.

MACMILLAN EDUCATION DO BRASIL
Av. Brigadeiro Faria Lima, 1.309, 3º Andar –
Jd. Paulistano – São Paulo – SP – 01452-002
www.macmillan.com.br
Customer Service: [55] (11) 4613-2278
0800 16 88 77
Fax: [55] (11) 4612-6098

Impresso no Brasil, Eskenazi, 12 2024